THE
BABY BORN AT
CHRISTMAS

Sally Ann Wright and Honor Ayres

Mary and the angel

A long time ago, there lived a girl called Mary.

One day an angel came to visit her.

'Don't be afraid,' said the angel. 'God has sent me to tell you that you are going to have a baby. You will call him Jesus and he will be God's son.'

Mary was amazed. But she told the angel she was ready to do whatever God wanted her to do.

Mary visits Elizabeth

Mary went to tell her cousin Elizabeth the good news.

'You are very special,' Elizabeth told her.

'God has chosen you to be mother of his own son.'

Then Elizabeth told her that she was also going to have a baby after many years of waiting.

Mary praised God for all the good things he was doing, and for choosing her for such an important job.

The road to Bethlehem

Mary stayed in the little village of Nazareth. She married Joseph, the village carpenter. Then, just at the time when her baby was due to be born, the Roman emperor ordered everyone to return to their home town so they could be counted.

Mary and Joseph had to travel to Bethlehem, a few days' walk away. Many other people were travelling along the same road.

No room at the inn

When they reached Bethlehem, Joseph tried to find a place where they could stay, but the town was very busy with all the visitors who had come to be counted.

That night, Mary gave birth to her baby son. She tore up strips of cloth to wrap him in and made a bed for him in the manger, because there was no room at the inn.

Out in the fields

That night there were shepherds in the fields nearby, looking after their sheep.

Suddenly the sky was filled with light and an angel appeared.

A message of good news

'Don't be afraid,' said the angel.
'I have good news for you.
Today in Bethlehem a saviour has been born.
You will know who he is, because you will find
him lying in a manger.'

The sound of many angels

Then the sky was filled with the sound of many angels,
all praising God for sending Jesus to be the saviour
of the world.

'Glory to God!' they sang. 'Peace to everyone on earth.'

The shepherds go to Bethlehem

When the angels had gone, the shepherds left their sheep and went to find the baby.

The baby in the manger

They found Mary and Joseph—
and there was the baby
lying in a manger, just as the
angel had said.

23

The new star in the heavens

That night, when Jesus was born in Bethlehem,
a new star appeared in the sky. As Mary
watched over her baby son, wise men,
far away in the east, saw the star and
wondered what it might mean.

Wise men go to worship

'A king has been born,' the wise men decided.
'We must go to worship him.'

So they prepared to set out on a journey to find the baby king.

They took with them gifts,
and followed the star.

Gifts for the baby king

The star guided the wise men to a house in Bethlehem, where they found the child with his mother, Mary.

When they saw Jesus, they knelt before him and offered him the gifts they had brought: gold, frankincense and myrrh.

Mary thought about what the angel and the shepherds had told her. She thought about the gifts of the wise men and about the child who was God's son, Jesus, the saviour of the world.

Barnabas for Children® is a registered device mark
of The Bible Reading Fellowship

Published by
The Bible Reading Fellowship
15 The Chambers, Vineyard
Abingdon, OX14 3FE
United Kingdom
Tel: +44 (0)1865 319700
Email: enquiries@brf.org.uk
Website: www.brf.org.uk
BRF is a Registered Charity

ISBN 978 0 85746 024 0

First edition 2008
This revised edition 2011

Copyright © 2011 Anno Domini Publishing
www.ad-publishing.com
Text copyright © 2011 Sally Ann Wright
Illustrations copyright © 2008 Honor Ayres

Publishing Director: Annette Reynolds
Art Director: Gerald Rogers
Pre-production Manager: Krystyna Kowalska Hewitt
Production Manager: John Laister

Printed and bound in Singapore